D1202356

Dedication

This journal is dedicated to kids,
to learn and tell their story in a safe
place that would allow them to grow
socially and emotionally.

This Journal
BELONGS TO

Name

_____

My Journal Writing Buddy is

_____

Selfie of you and your writing buddy

Me	My Buddy

If this Journal is lost, please call

_____

Meet the Bayside Bunch

The Bayside Bunch is a group of friends that grew up together in a small community in New York. They enjoy playing outside games (running, jumping, climbing, etc.) filled with laughter and big smiles throughout the year. The outside games and their many adventures teach kindness, courage, dedication, honesty, respect for all, and many other character traits. In addition, the kids learn about the importance of working together despite any challenges that may come their way.

The Bayside Bunch attends P.S. 411 Elementary, a small school where the teachers and staff are caring. In this school, kids learn about themselves and the world around them. The school setting gives kids access to discover what's possible in a safe space to learn and grow. Kids travel on field trips and read stories that take them to places outside their small community. This unique experience helps the Bayside Bunch find their voices in a supportive environment. Teachers and staff support the kids by listening and guiding them on a path of empowerment. The school and community experiences build character for the Bayside Bunch. Kids use the experiences to make healthy decisions in and out of their school community.

Table of Contents

ALL ABOUT ME!

My name is

I am _____ years old.

My Favorite song

My Best Friend...

My Dream

My Favorite color is...

My Favorite Sport

My Favorite food...

My Favorite Game

Pet name

The Bayside Bunch
Kindness Pledge

I pledge to use kind words
and actions.

I pledge to be thankful and
positive every day.

I pledge to be respectful
and share my smile with all
people.

I pledge to be a good friend
and neighbor every day.

I pledge to be kind!

Kindness MATTERS

My Writing Buddy,
Bubba

On one spring day, Selwyn's parents took him to the local pet store for his birthday. They walked around the pet store for the perfect birthday gift. Selwyn noticed a goldfish that jumped and moved around the other fish in the tank. The fish splashed water on the floor. Suddenly, Selwyn walked over to the fish tank with a big smile. He saw a small black and orange fish that smiled. Selwyn pleaded with his parents to buy the black and orange goldfish. Selwyn was happy with his birthday gift.

Selwyn is a kind and popular kid at school. He enjoys reading the morning news at P.S. 411 Elementary. Selwyn enjoys talking about school events and welcoming new kids. Many kids are happy to hear Selwyn read the morning news. Selwyn prepares the morning news by practicing his sight words and writing with Bubba , his new buddy. Bubba is a great listener. He helps Selwyn keep a calm body, hands, feet, and thinking. Bubba builds Selwyn's confidence to read the morning news at school each day.

MY DAILY JOURNAL

Today is _____

The weather was ☀️ ☁️ 🌬️ ⛅ 🌧️ ❄️

I was feeling 😌 😍 😲 😎 😔 😮 😂

Circle three positive words that describe you today

Brave	Joyful	Intelligent	Super	Kind
Leader	Happy	Friendly	Honest	Courageous
Responsible	Amazing	Cheerful	Caring	Trustworthy
Considerate	Great	Smart	Strong	Awesome
Respectful	Compassionate	Helpful	Dedicated	Love

What was the best part of your day?

Draw a picture of how you feel today?

Today my biggest challenge was

_____

What was the best solution to solve my challenge?

_____

Suggestions

Talk to a friend	Exercise
Talk with an adult	Go for a walk
Write in my journal	Cool off
Take a deep breath	Listen
Think before reacting	Consider someone's point of view

What do you want to remember about today?

_____

_____

_____

_____

_____

_____

_____

_____

If you had $1, what would you buy and why?

_____

_____

Draw or write about it below.

What can you learn from this experience?

_____

_____

What do you want to be when you graduate from school and why?

_____

_____

Draw or write about it below.

How are you going to start planning today?

_____

_____

MY DAILY JOURNAL

Today is _____

The weather was ☀️ ⛅ 🌬️ ☁️ 🌧️ ❄️

I was feeling 😌 😍 😳 😎 😔 😮 😂

Circle three positive words that describe you today

Brave	Joyful	Intelligent	Super	Kind
Leader	Happy	Friendly	Honest	Courageous
Responsible	Amazing	Cheerful	Caring	Trustworthy
Considerate	Great	Smart	Strong	Awesome
Respectful	Compassionate	Helpful	Dedicated	Love

What was the best part of your day?

Draw a picture of how you feel today?

Today my biggest challenge was

_____

What was the best solution to solve my challenge?

_____

Suggestions

Talk to a friend	Exercise
Talk with an adult	Go for a walk
Write in my journal	Cool off
Take a deep breath	Listen
Think before reacting	Consider someone's point of view

What do you want to remember about today?

_____

_____

_____

_____

_____

_____

_____

_____

Who is your favorite teacher in school?

_____

_____

Draw or write about it below.

What do you like most about them?

_____

_____

Describe one place you would like to travel to someday. Who would travel with you?

_____

_____

Draw or write about it below.

Why would you want to travel with this person?

_____

_____

MY DAILY JOURNAL

Today is _____

The weather was

I was feeling

Circle three positive words that describe you today

Brave	Joyful	Intelligent	Super	Kind
Leader	Happy	Friendly	Honest	Courageous
Responsible	Amazing	Cheerful	Caring	Trustworthy
Considerate	Great	Smart	Strong	Awesome
Respectful	Compassionate	Helpful	Dedicated	Love

What was the best part of your day?

Draw a picture of how you feel today?

Today my biggest challenge was

_____

What was the best solution to solve my challenge?

_____

Suggestions

Talk to a friend	Exercise
Talk with an adult	Go for a walk
Write in my journal	Cool off
Take a deep breath	Listen
Think before reacting	Consider someone's point of view

What do you want to remember about today?

_____

_____

_____

_____

_____

_____

_____

If you could travel the world, what areas would you visit?

_____

_____

Draw or write about it below.

What do you enjoy about the area?

_____

_____

If you were helping plan a school field trip, where would you want to go?

_____

_____

Draw or write about it below.

What do you enjoy about the area?

_____

_____

What is your favorite holiday?

_____

_____

Draw or write about it below.

Why do you like it so much?

_____

_____

MY DAILY JOURNAL

Today is _____

The weather was ☀️ ⛅ 🌬️ 🌥️ 🌧️ ❄️

I was feeling ☺️ 😍 😲 😎 😌 😮 😂

Circle three positive words that describe you today

Brave	Joyful	Intelligent	Super	Kind
Leader	Happy	Friendly	Honest	Courageous
Responsible	Amazing	Cheerful	Caring	Trustworthy
Considerate	Great	Smart	Strong	Awesome
Respectful	Compassionate	Helpful	Dedicated	Love

What was the best part of your day?

Draw a picture of how you feel today?

Today my biggest challenge was

_____

What was the best solution to solve my challenge?

_____

Suggestions

Talk to a friend	Exercise
Talk with an adult	Go for a walk
Write in my journal	Cool off
Take a deep breath	Listen
Think before reacting	Consider someone's point of view

What do you want to remember about today?

_____

_____

_____

_____

_____

_____

_____

_____

If you had two wishes, what would they be?

_____

_____

Draw or write about it below.

Who would you tell?

_____

_____

Can you dream of a kinder world?

Fun Activity

Try a

Design your own bookmark

Let someone know how special they are by sharing a bookmark.

• Use the preprinted bookmarks on the following page to design and color images to share with friends and family.

• You will never lose track of your reading place or writing again.

Materials:
Crayons, Pencil, Marker, scissor

Kindness	Courage	Happiness	Dedication

Imagine you've found a time machine! Where would you like to travel?

_____

_____

Draw or write about it below.

What do you enjoy about the area?

_____

_____

What is one word that makes you happy?

_____

_____

Draw or write about it below.

How would you share this feeling with your family or friends?

_____

_____

MY DAILY JOURNAL

Today is _____

The weather was ☀️ ☁️ 🌬️ ⛅ 🌧️ ❄️

I was feeling 😊 😍 😲 😎 😔 😮 😂

Circle three positive words that describe you today

Brave	Joyful	Intelligent	Super	Kind
Leader	Happy	Friendly	Honest	Courageous
Responsible	Amazing	Cheerful	Caring	Trustworthy
Considerate	Great	Smart	Strong	Awesome
Respectful	Compassionate	Helpful	Dedicated	Love

What was the best part of your day?

Draw a picture of how you feel today?

Today my biggest challenge was

_____

What was the best solution to solve my challenge?

_____

Suggestions

Talk to a friend	Exercise
Talk with an adult	Go for a walk
Write in my journal	Cool off
Take a deep breath	Listen
Think before reacting	Consider someone's point of view

What do you want to remember about today?

_____

_____

_____

_____

_____

_____

_____

_____

What are some of your favorite animals in the zoo?

_____

_____

Draw or write about it below.

What do you like about them?

_____

_____

What are your favorite things to do during summer vacation with your family?

_____

_____

Draw or write about it below.

How does family time make you feel?

_____

_____

MY DAILY JOURNAL

Today is _____

The weather was ☀️ ☁️ 🌬️ ☁️ 🌧️ ❄️

I was feeling 😌 😍 😮 😎 😔 😲 😂

Circle three positive words that describe you today

Brave	Joyful	Intelligent	Super	Kind
Leader	Happy	Friendly	Honest	Courageous
Responsible	Amazing	Cheerful	Caring	Trustworthy
Considerate	Great	Smart	Strong	Awesome
Respectful	Compassionate	Helpful	Dedicated	Love

What was the best part of your day?

Draw a picture of how you feel today?

Today my biggest challenge was

_____

What was the best solution to solve my challenge?

_____

Suggestions

Talk to a friend	Exercise
Talk with an adult	Go for a walk
Write in my journal	Cool off
Take a deep breath	Listen
Think before reacting	Consider someone's point of view

What do you want to remember about today?

_____

_____

_____

_____

_____

_____

_____

_____

Try a
Fun Activity

Let's create a Kindness Jar for a friend

Write the name of a kind person on the top line.
Explain how they share kindness on the next line.
Draw a picture of a friend being kind.
Material: Pencil, Pen, Markers, Crayons

What did you enjoy about the activity?

_____

_____

How did it make you feel?

_____

_____

Try a
Fun Activity
Kindness Challenge

Using the Word List on the following page,
circle 50 **kind words** that you would say
to a friend and family member.

```
D  Z  B  E  A  U  T  I  F  U  L  P  F  E  C  P  B  C  T  D
K  E  Y  P  T  Q  B  J  N  S  S  A  A  S  A  L  R  O  T  U
E  H  L  E  P  E  U  T  I  M  T  T  I  U  L  E  A  M  J  H
V  R  E  I  C  L  R  H  C  A  R  I  R  P  M  A  V  P  C  O
A  E  H  L  G  O  E  R  E  R  O  E  H  P  R  S  E  A  H  N
L  S  S  A  P  H  U  A  I  T  N  N  O  O  E  A  U  S  E  E
U  P  I  A  P  F  T  R  S  F  G  T  N  R  F  N  N  S  E  S
A  E  N  I  M  P  U  F  A  U  I  Z  O  T  L  T  D  I  R  T
B  C  C  X  K  T  Y  L  U  G  R  C  R  I  E  R  E  O  F  W
L  T  E  A  D  O  R  A  B  L  E  E  A  V  C  U  R  N  U  O
E  F  R  G  E  N  E  R  O  U  S  X  B  E  T  S  S  A  L  N
U  U  E  D  F  R  I  E  N  D  L  Y  L  S  I  T  T  T  C  D
H  L  C  D  E  P  E  N  D  A  B  L  E  O  V  W  A  E  L  E
P  E  R  F  E  C  T  C  A  R  I  N  G  I  E  O  N  L  E  R
G  R  A  T  E  F  U  L  Z  P  O  L  I  T  E  R  D  G  V  F
I  L  O  V  I  N  G  P  J  O  Y  P  O  S  I  T  I  V  E  U
F  O  E  S  A  M  A  Z  I  N  G  K  I  N  D  H  N  I  R  L
T  Y  O  J  C  O  N  S  I  D  E  R  A  T  E  Y  G  O  O  D
E  A  T  H  O  U  G  H  T  F  U  L  G  E  N  T  L  E  I  O
D  L  I  N  T  E  L  L  I  G  E  N  T  K  L  E  A  D  E  R
```

WORD LIST:

ADORABLE	FAIR	KIND	sincere
AMAZING	FRIENDLY	LEADER	SMART
BEAUTIFUL	GENEROUS	LOVING	STRONG
BRAVE	GENTLE	LOYAL	SUPPORTIVE
CALM	GIFTED	NICE	TERRIFIC
CARING	GOOD	PATIENT	THOUGHTFUL
CHEERFUL	GRATEFUL	PERFECT	TRUSTWORTHY
CLEVER	HAPPY	PLEASANT	UNDERSTANDING
COMPASSIONATE	HELPFUL	PLEASURE	VALUABLE
CONSIDERATE	HONEST	POLITE	WONDERFUL
COURAGE	HONORABLE	POSITIVE	
DELIGHTFUL	INTELLIGENT	REFLECTIVE	
DEPENDABLE	JOY	RESPECTFUL	

How would you use kind words in school and at home?

_____

_____

_____

_____

My Day Begins with a
Smile

Grace enjoys talking with her friends about community projects to keep everyone safe and healthy. For example, she prepares the recycling bin at home by separating the paper and plastic items into the correct bin. She encourages friends and family members to keep their community clean. Grace believes that recycling will change the world.

Grace is the president of the student government at P.S. 411 Elementary. She is always thinking about ways to change the world. Grace is involved in the school's recycling program and encourages kids to keep the school clean. She is known as a caring, confident, and trustworthy kid.

MY DAILY JOURNAL

Today is _____

The weather was ☀️ ⛅ 🌬️ ☁️ 🌧️ ❄️

I was feeling 🙂 😍 😳 😎 😔 😮 😂

Circle three positive words that describe you today

Brave	Joyful	Intelligent	Super	Kind
Leader	Happy	Friendly	Honest	Courageous
Responsible	Amazing	Cheerful	Caring	Trustworthy
Considerate	Great	Smart	Strong	Awesome
Respectful	Compassionate	Helpful	Dedicated	Love

What was the best part of your day?

Draw a picture of how you feel today?

Today my biggest challenge was

_____

What was the best solution to solve my challenge?

_____

Suggestions

Talk to a friend	Exercise
Talk with an adult	Go for a walk
Write in my journal	Cool off
Take a deep breath	Listen
Think before reacting	Consider someone's point of view

What do you want to remember about today?

_____

_____

_____

_____

_____

_____

_____

_____

What is your favorite television show?

_____

_____

Draw or write about it below.

Why do you think people should watch it?

_____

_____

What is your favorite book?

_____

_____

Draw or write about it below.

Why do you enjoy reading the story?

_____

_____

MY DAILY JOURNAL

Today is _____

The weather was ☀️ ☁️ 🌬️ ⛅ 🌧️ ❄️

I was feeling 😌 😍 😳 😎 😔 😮 😂

Circle three positive words that describe you today

Brave	Joyful	Intelligent	Super	Kind
Leader	Happy	Friendly	Honest	Courageous
Responsible	Amazing	Cheerful	Caring	Trustworthy
Considerate	Great	Smart	Strong	Awesome
Respectful	Compassionate	Helpful	Dedicated	Love

What was the best part of your day?

Draw a picture of how you feel today?

Today my biggest challenge was

_____

What was the best solution to solve my challenge?

_____

Suggestions

Talk to a friend	Exercise
Talk with an adult	Go for a walk
Write in my journal	Cool off
Take a deep breath	Listen
Think before reacting	Consider someone's point of view

What do you want to remember about today?

_____

_____

_____

_____

_____

_____

_____

_____

What types of games would you create for kids if you were building a new playground?

_____

_____

Draw or write about it below.

What would be your favorite game?

_____

_____

Imagine you get a magic hat for your birthday. What happens when you wear the hat?

_____

_____

Draw or write about it below.

How does the hat make you feel?

_____

_____

MY DAILY JOURNAL

Today is _____

The weather was ☀️ ⛅ 🌬️ ☁️ 🌧️ ❄️

I was feeling 😊 😍 😮 😎 😔 😲 😂

Circle three positive words that describe you today

Brave	Joyful	Intelligent	Super	Kind
Leader	Happy	Friendly	Honest	Courageous
Responsible	Amazing	Cheerful	Caring	Trustworthy
Considerate	Great	Smart	Strong	Awesome
Respectful	Compassionate	Helpful	Dedicated	Love

What was the best part of your day?

Draw a picture of how you feel today?

Today my biggest challenge was

_____

What was the best solution to solve my challenge?

_____

Suggestions

Talk to a friend	Exercise
Talk with an adult	Go for a walk
Write in my journal	Cool off
Take a deep breath	Listen
Think before reacting	Consider someone's point of view

What do you want to remember about today?

_____

_____

_____

_____

_____

_____

_____

_____

Courage Conquers Fear

Fun Activity

Kindness Activity

• Make your own thank you card for a friend or family member.

• Decorate the card below with a drawing, magazine pictures or stickers.

THANK YOU	Dear _____
	Thank you for
	_____
	_____
	It made me feel
	_____
	_____
	From
	_____

What would be your first reaction if you received an invitation to have lunch with the school principal?

_____

_____

Draw or write about it below.

How would you feel?

_____

_____

If you were drawing a school map for a new kid at your school, what are three places they should know?

_____ ✏

_____

Draw or write about it below.

Why are the places important to you?

_____

_____

MY DAILY JOURNAL

Today is _____

The weather was ☀️ ☁️ 🌬️ ⛅ 🌧️ ❄️

I was feeling 😌 😍 😲 😎 😔 😮 😂

Circle three positive words that describe you today

Brave	Joyful	Intelligent	Super	Kind
Leader	Happy	Friendly	Honest	Courageous
Responsible	Amazing	Cheerful	Caring	Trustworthy
Considerate	Great	Smart	Strong	Awesome
Respectful	Compassionate	Helpful	Dedicated	Love

What was the best part of your day?

Draw a picture of how you feel today?

Today my biggest challenge was

_____

What was the best solution to solve my challenge?

_____

Suggestions

Talk to a friend	Exercise
Talk with an adult	Go for a walk
Write in my journal	Cool off
Take a deep breath	Listen
Think before reacting	Consider someone's point of view

What do you want to remember about today?

_____

_____

_____

_____

_____

_____

_____

_____

What is one goal you accomplished yesterday?

_____

_____

Draw or write about it below.

How did it make you feel?

_____

_____

What is one place you enjoy visiting outside of school?

_____

_____

Draw or write about it below.

What do you enjoy about the area?

_____

_____

MY DAILY JOURNAL

Today is _____

The weather was

I was feeling

Circle three positive words that describe you today

Brave	Joyful	Intelligent	Super	Kind
Leader	Happy	Friendly	Honest	Courageous
Responsible	Amazing	Cheerful	Caring	Trustworthy
Considerate	Great	Smart	Strong	Awesome
Respectful	Compassionate	Helpful	Dedicated	Love

What was the best part of your day?

Draw a picture of how you feel today?

Today my biggest challenge was

_____

What was the best solution to solve my challenge?

_____

Suggestions

Talk to a friend	Exercise
Talk with an adult	Go for a walk
Write in my journal	Cool off
Take a deep breath	Listen
Think before reacting	Consider someone's point of view

What do you want to remember about today?

_____

_____

_____

_____

_____

_____

_____

_____

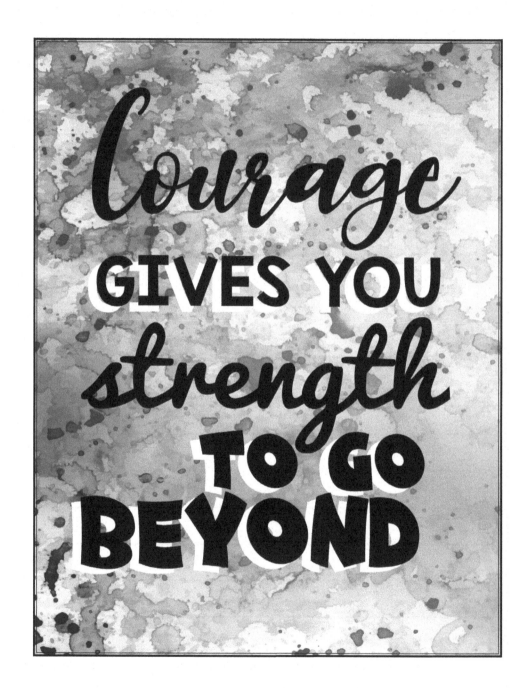

What is your best memory of spending the day with your family?

_____

_____

Draw or write about it below.

How did it make you feel?

_____

_____

If you closed your eyes and listened to the world around you, what sounds would you hear?

_____

_____

Draw or write about it below.

How did it make you feel?

_____

_____

What is the name of a person that you admire?

_____

_____

Draw or write about it below.

What do you know about them?

_____

_____

MY DAILY JOURNAL

Today is _____

The weather was ☀ ⛅ 🌬 ☁ 🌧 ❄

I was feeling 😌 😍 😲 😎 😔 😮 😂

Circle three positive words that describe you today

Brave	Joyful	Intelligent	Super	Kind
Leader	Happy	Friendly	Honest	Courageous
Responsible	Amazing	Cheerful	Caring	Trustworthy
Considerate	Great	Smart	Strong	Awesome
Respectful	Compassionate	Helpful	Dedicated	Love

What was the best part of your day?

Draw a picture of how you feel today?

Today my biggest challenge was

_____

What was the best solution to solve my challenge?

_____

Suggestions

Talk to a friend	Exercise
Talk with an adult	Go for a walk
Write in my journal	Cool off
Take a deep breath	Listen
Think before reacting	Consider someone's point of view

What do you want to remember about today?

_____

_____

_____

_____

_____

_____

_____

_____

What makes you laugh?

_____

_____

Draw or write about it below.

How does it make you feel?

_____

_____

Fun Activity
Try a

Let's be courageous and try a new **fruit** and **vegetable.**

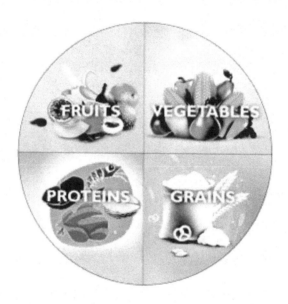

What is the name of the new fruit?

_____

What is the name of the new vegetable?

_____

How do the new food items make you feel?

_____

Dedication

Taking an
Adventure

Chico talks about the adventures of visiting parks. He believes that there are many safe and fun outdoor activities for kids. The outdoor experiences can help build friendship in a safe space over time. Chico is interested in collecting stamps from the parks to include in his travel journal. It records his journey and serves as a great memory to share with his friends over a lifetime.

Chico enjoys playing video games and reading comic books during his free time. He is a collector of old and new comic books. Chico is always excited to talk about the video games and storylines from the comic books with the Bayside Bunch. The adventures build courage and confidence which helps Chico put aside his fear of failure and the unknown.

MY DAILY JOURNAL

Today is _____

The weather was ☀ ⛅ 🌬 ⛅ 🌧 ❄

I was feeling 😌 😍 😳 😎 😔 😮 😂

Circle three positive words that describe you today

Brave	Joyful	Intelligent	Super	Kind
Leader	Happy	Friendly	Honest	Courageous
Responsible	Amazing	Cheerful	Caring	Trustworthy
Considerate	Great	Smart	Strong	Awesome
Respectful	Compassionate	Helpful	Dedicated	Love

What was the best part of your day?

Draw a picture of how you feel today?

Today my biggest challenge was

_____

What was the best solution to solve my challenge?

_____

Suggestions

Talk to a friend	Exercise
Talk with an adult	Go for a walk
Write in my journal	Cool off
Take a deep breath	Listen
Think before reacting	Consider someone's point of view

What do you want to remember about today?

_____

_____

_____

_____

_____

_____

_____

_____

What is one accomplishment you've reached today?

_____

_____

Draw or write about it below.

Why are you proud of it?

_____

_____

What is your favorite chore to complete at home?

_____

_____

Draw or write about it below.

How does it make you feel?

_____

_____

MY DAILY JOURNAL

Today is _____

The weather was ☀️ ⛅ 🌬️ ☁️ 🌧️ ❄️

I was feeling 😌 😍 😲 😎 😔 😮 😂

Circle three positive words that describe you today

Brave	Joyful	Intelligent	Super	Kind
Leader	Happy	Friendly	Honest	Courageous
Responsible	Amazing	Cheerful	Caring	Trustworthy
Considerate	Great	Smart	Strong	Awesome
Respectful	Compassionate	Helpful	Dedicated	Love

What was the best part of your day?

Draw a picture of how you feel today?

Today my biggest challenge was

_____

What was the best solution to solve my challenge?

_____

Suggestions

Talk to a friend	Exercise
Talk with an adult	Go for a walk
Write in my journal	Cool off
Take a deep breath	Listen
Think before reacting	Consider someone's point of view

What do you want to remember about today?

_____

_____

_____

_____

_____

_____

_____

_____

What is the name of your favorite teacher?

_____

_____

Draw or write about it below.

What makes them unique?

_____

_____

What is your favorite color?

_____

_____

Draw or write about it below.

How does it make you feel?

_____

_____

MY DAILY JOURNAL

Today is _____

The weather was ☀ ⛅ 🌬 ☁ 🌧 ❄

I was feeling 😊 😍 😮 😎 😔 😲 😂

Circle three positive words that describe you today

Brave	Joyful	Intelligent	Super	Kind
Leader	Happy	Friendly	Honest	Courageous
Responsible	Amazing	Cheerful	Caring	Trustworthy
Considerate	Great	Smart	Strong	Awesome
Respectful	Compassionate	Helpful	Dedicated	Love

What was the best part of your day?

Draw a picture of how you feel today?

Today my biggest challenge was

_____

What was the best solution to solve my challenge?

_____

Suggestions

Talk to a friend	Exercise
Talk with an adult	Go for a walk
Write in my journal	Cool off
Take a deep breath	Listen
Think before reacting	Consider someone's point of view

What do you want to remember about today?

_____

_____

_____

_____

_____

_____

_____

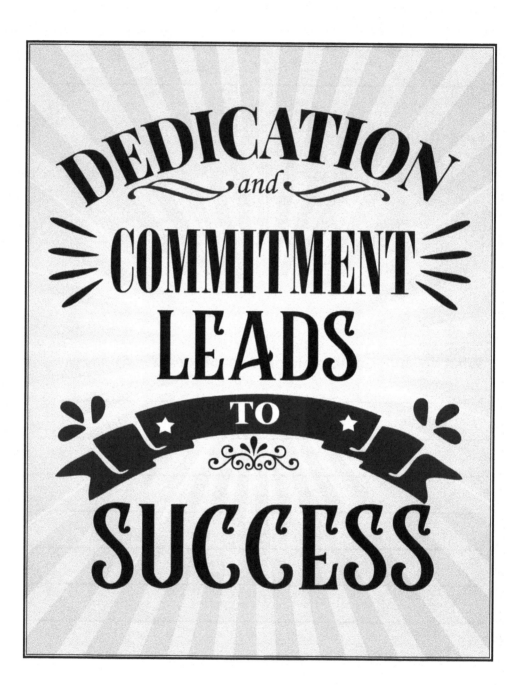

Write down three ways to help a friend at school today?

_____

_____

Draw or write about it below.

How does it make you feel?

_____

_____

What is the best advice someone has given to you?

_____

_____

Draw or write about it below.

What can you learn from this experience?

_____

_____

What is your favorite ice cream flavor?

_____

_____

Draw or write about it below.

How does it make you feel?

_____

_____

MY DAILY JOURNAL

Today is _____

The weather was ☀️ ⛅ 🌬️ ☁️ 🌧️ ❄️

I was feeling 🙃 😍 😳 😎 😔 😮 😂

Circle three positive words that describe you today

Brave	Joyful	Intelligent	Super	Kind
Leader	Happy	Friendly	Honest	Courageous
Responsible	Amazing	Cheerful	Caring	Trustworthy
Considerate	Great	Smart	Strong	Awesome
Respectful	Compassionate	Helpful	Dedicated	Love

What was the best part of your day?

Draw a picture of how you feel today?

Today my biggest challenge was

_____

What was the best solution to solve my challenge?

_____

Suggestions

Talk to a friend	Exercise
Talk with an adult	Go for a walk
Write in my journal	Cool off
Take a deep breath	Listen
Think before reacting	Consider someone's point of view

What do you want to remember about today?

_____

_____

_____

_____

_____

_____

_____

_____

When you are angry, what helps you to calm down?

_____

_____

Draw or write about it below.

How does it make you feel?

_____

_____

HARDWORK & DEDICATION

What do you remember about the last day of school?

_____

_____

Draw or write about it below.

How did it make you feel?

_____

_____

How do you celebrate your birthday?

_____

_____

Draw or write about it below.

How does it make you feel?

_____

_____

MY DAILY JOURNAL

Today is _____

The weather was ☀️ ☁️ 🌬️ ☁️ 🌧️ ❄️

I was feeling 🙂 😍 😳 😎 😔 😮 😂

Circle three positive words that describe you today

Brave	Joyful	Intelligent	Super	Kind
Leader	Happy	Friendly	Honest	Courageous
Responsible	Amazing	Cheerful	Caring	Trustworthy
Considerate	Great	Smart	Strong	Awesome
Respectful	Compassionate	Helpful	Dedicated	Love

What was the best part of your day?

Draw a picture of how you feel today?

Today my biggest challenge was

_____

What was the best solution to solve my challenge?

_____

Suggestions

Talk to a friend	Exercise
Talk with an adult	Go for a walk
Write in my journal	Cool off
Take a deep breath	Listen
Think before reacting	Consider someone's point of view

What do you want to remember about today?

_____

_____

_____

_____

_____

_____

_____

_____

What is the name of your favorite green vegetable?

_____

_____

Draw or write about it below.

How does it make you feel?

_____

_____

What is the name of your favorite fruit?

_____

_____

Draw or write about it below.

How would you share this experience with a friend or family member?

_____

_____

MY DAILY JOURNAL

Today is _____

The weather was ☀ ⛅ 🌬 ⛅ 🌧 ❄

I was feeling 😊 😍 😮 😎 😔 😲 😂

Circle three positive words that describe you today

Brave	Joyful	Intelligent	Super	Kind
Leader	Happy	Friendly	Honest	Courageous
Responsible	Amazing	Cheerful	Caring	Trustworthy
Considerate	Great	Smart	Strong	Awesome
Respectful	Compassionate	Helpful	Dedicated	Love

What was the best part of your day?

Draw a picture of how you feel today?

Today my biggest challenge was

_____

What was the best solution to solve my challenge?

_____

Suggestions

Talk to a friend	Exercise
Talk with an adult	Go for a walk
Write in my journal	Cool off
Take a deep breath	Listen
Think before reacting	Consider someone's point of view

What do you want to remember about today?

_____

_____

_____

_____

_____

_____

_____

_____

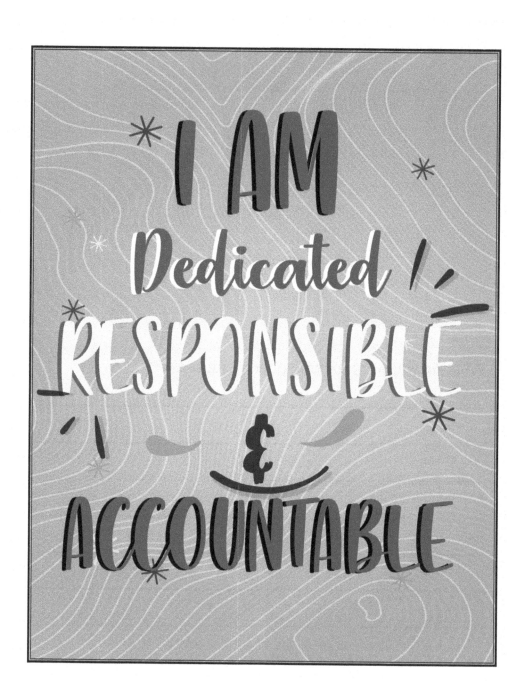

Fun Activity

List 4 chores that you are responsible and
dedicated to completing each day.

1. _____

2. _____

3. _____

4. _____

Draw a picture of you completing a chore at home.

How does that chore make you feel?

_____

I am Ready to Make
Good Choices

QB is learning about the game of chess at the local community barbershop. He recognizes the connection between chess moves and making healthy decisions. QB believes that all chess moves require patience, reflection, and calculations. The strategies from chess are used to help QB understand the world around him. He is a good listener and occasionally gives feedback to the Bayside Bunch.

QB enjoys math and science activities at P.S. 411 Elementary. He is a member of the Junior Tech Buddies at school. QB combines his chess, math, and science abilities to help kids solve technology problems around the school building.

MY DAILY JOURNAL

Today is _____

The weather was ☀️ 🌤️ 🌬️ ☁️ 🌧️ ❄️

I was feeling 😌 😍 😮 😎 😔 😯 😂

Circle three positive words that describe you today

Brave	Joyful	Intelligent	Super	Kind
Leader	Happy	Friendly	Honest	Courageous
Responsible	Amazing	Cheerful	Caring	Trustworthy
Considerate	Great	Smart	Strong	Awesome
Respectful	Compassionate	Helpful	Dedicated	Love

What was the best part of your day?

Draw a picture of how you feel today?

Today my biggest challenge was

_____

What was the best solution to solve my challenge?

_____

Suggestions

Talk to a friend	Exercise
Talk with an adult	Go for a walk
Write in my journal	Cool off
Take a deep breath	Listen
Think before reacting	Consider someone's point of view

What do you want to remember about today?

_____

_____

_____

_____

_____

_____

_____

_____

What would you say if you could tell your parent one thing that's been on your mind today?

_____

_____

Draw or write about it below.

How does it make you feel?

_____

_____

What is the coolest thing you learned with your friends?

_____

_____

Draw or write about it below.

How does it make you feel?

_____

_____

MY DAILY JOURNAL

Today is _____

The weather was ☀️ ☁️ 🌬️ ⛅ 🌧️ ❄️

I was feeling 😌 😍 😳 😎 😔 😮 😂

Circle three positive words that describe you today

Brave	Joyful	Intelligent	Super	Kind
Leader	Happy	Friendly	Honest	Courageous
Responsible	Amazing	Cheerful	Caring	Trustworthy
Considerate	Great	Smart	Strong	Awesome
Respectful	Compassionate	Helpful	Dedicated	Love

What was the best part of your day?

_____
_____
_____
_____
_____
_____
_____

Draw a picture of how you feel today?

Today my biggest challenge was

_____

What was the best solution to solve my challenge?

_____

Suggestions

Talk to a friend	Exercise
Talk with an adult	Go for a walk
Write in my journal	Cool off
Take a deep breath	Listen
Think before reacting	Consider someone's point of view

What do you want to remember about today?

_____

_____

_____

_____

_____

_____

_____

_____

What are you grateful for today and why?

_____

_____

Draw or write about it below.

How does it make you feel?

_____

_____

What does the word kindness mean to you?

_____

_____

Draw or write about it below.

How does it make you feel?

_____

_____

MY DAILY JOURNAL

Today is _____

The weather was ☀️ ☁️ 🌬️ ⛅ 🌧️ ❄️

I was feeling 😊 😍 😳 😎 😔 😮 😂

Circle three positive words that describe you today

Brave	Joyful	Intelligent	Super	Kind
Leader	Happy	Friendly	Honest	Courageous
Responsible	Amazing	Cheerful	Caring	Trustworthy
Considerate	Great	Smart	Strong	Awesome
Respectful	Compassionate	Helpful	Dedicated	Love

What was the best part of your day?

Draw a picture of how you feel today?

Today my biggest challenge was

_____

What was the best solution to solve my challenge?

_____

Suggestions

Talk to a friend	Exercise
Talk with an adult	Go for a walk
Write in my journal	Cool off
Take a deep breath	Listen
Think before reacting	Consider someone's point of view

What do you want to remember about today?

_____

_____

_____

_____

_____

_____

_____

_____

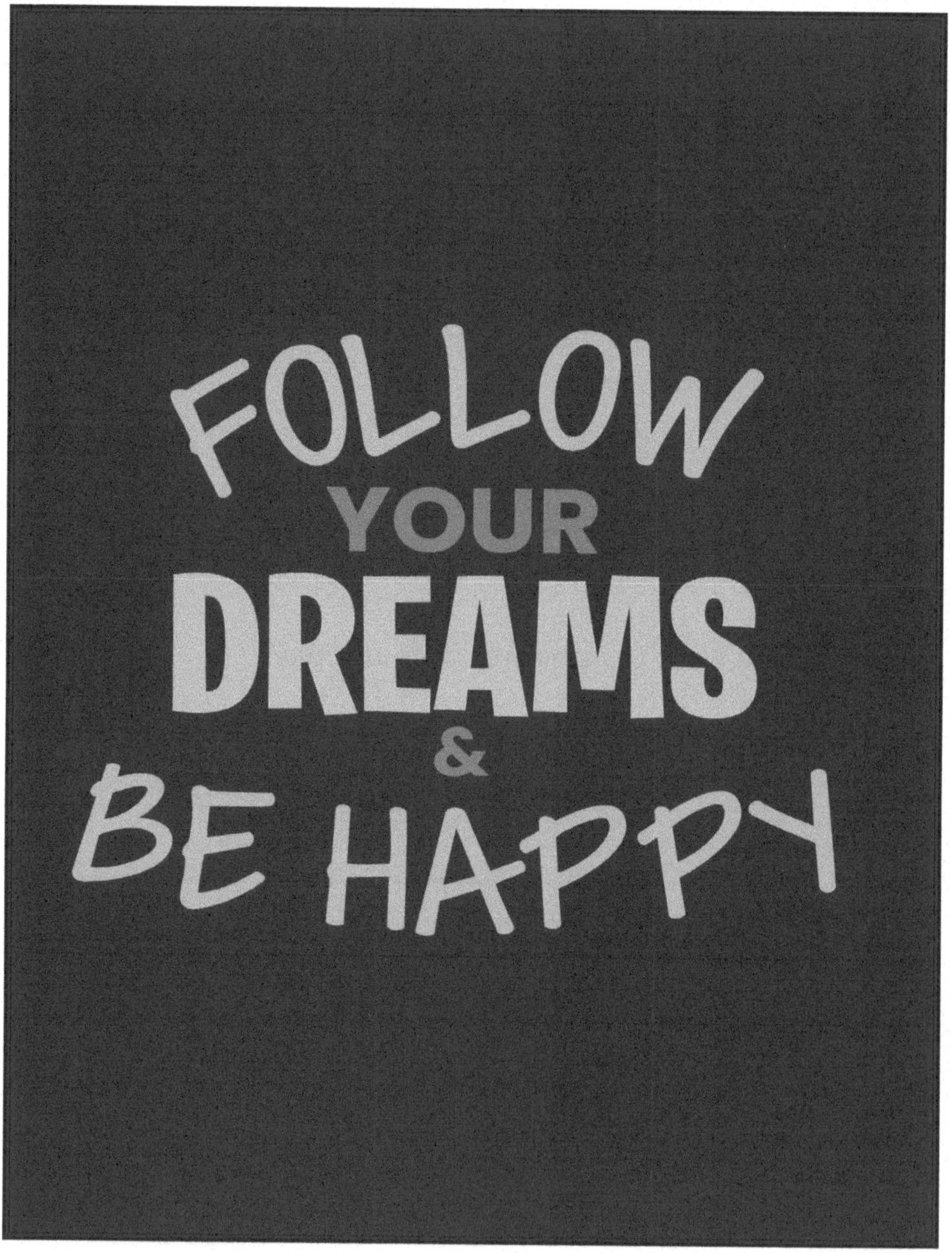
FOLLOW
YOUR
DREAMS
&
BE HAPPY

Fun Activity
Try a

Create your own
Hopes & Dreams Vision Board

How does the vision board make you feel?

_____

What does dedication mean to you?

_____

_____

Draw or write about it below.

How does it make you feel?

_____

_____

What makes you happy?

_____

_____

Draw or write about it below.

How does it make you feel?

_____

_____

MY DAILY JOURNAL

Today is _____

The weather was ☀️ 🌤️ 🌬️ ⛅ 🌧️ ❄️

I was feeling 😊 😍 😲 😎 😌 😮 😂

Circle three positive words that describe you today

Brave	Joyful	Intelligent	Super	Kind
Leader	Happy	Friendly	Honest	Courageous
Responsible	Amazing	Cheerful	Caring	Trustworthy
Considerate	Great	Smart	Strong	Awesome
Respectful	Compassionate	Helpful	Dedicated	Love

What was the best part of your day?

Draw a picture of how you feel today?

Today my biggest challenge was

_____

What was the best solution to solve my challenge?

_____

Suggestions

Talk to a friend	Exercise
Talk with an adult	Go for a walk
Write in my journal	Cool off
Take a deep breath	Listen
Think before reacting	Consider someone's point of view

What do you want to remember about today?

_____

_____

_____

_____

_____

_____

_____

_____

What are three essential safety tips every kid should know to stay safe?

_____

_____

Draw or write about it below.

How does it make you feel?

_____

_____

What do you think would be a great birthday gift for your parent?

_____

_____

Draw or write about it below.

Why is the gift important to you?

_____

_____

MY DAILY JOURNAL

Today is _____

The weather was ☀️ ⛅ 🌬️ ⛅ 🌧️ ❄️

I was feeling 😌 😍 😳 😎 😔 😮 😂

Circle three positive words that describe you today

Brave	Joyful	Intelligent	Super	Kind
Leader	Happy	Friendly	Honest	Courageous
Responsible	Amazing	Cheerful	Caring	Trustworthy
Considerate	Great	Smart	Strong	Awesome
Respectful	Compassionate	Helpful	Dedicated	Love

What was the best part of your day?

Draw a picture of how you feel today?

Today my biggest challenge was

_____

What was the best solution to solve my challenge?

_____

Suggestions

Talk to a friend	Exercise
Talk with an adult	Go for a walk
Write in my journal	Cool off
Take a deep breath	Listen
Think before reacting	Consider someone's point of view

What do you want to remember about today?

_____

_____

_____

_____

_____

_____

_____

_____

What was your best memory of kindergarten?

_____

_____

Draw or write about it below.

What did you learn from this experience?

_____

_____

What is one mistake you made yesterday?

_____

_____

Draw or write about it below.

What would you do differently today?

_____

_____

Do you get bored quickly? What are three activities to help you overcome the feeling?

_____

_____

Draw or write about it below.

How would you share this experience with a friend or family member?

_____

_____

MY DAILY JOURNAL

Today is _____

The weather was ☀️ ☁️ 🌬️ ⛅ 🌧️ ❄️

I was feeling 😌 😍 😳 😎 😔 😮 😂

Circle three positive words that describe you today

Brave	Joyful	Intelligent	Super	Kind
Leader	Happy	Friendly	Honest	Courageous
Responsible	Amazing	Cheerful	Caring	Trustworthy
Considerate	Great	Smart	Strong	Awesome
Respectful	Compassionate	Helpful	Dedicated	Love

What was the best part of your day?

Draw a picture of how you feel today?

Today my biggest challenge was

_____

What was the best solution to solve my challenge?

_____

Suggestions

Talk to a friend	Exercise
Talk with an adult	Go for a walk
Write in my journal	Cool off
Take a deep breath	Listen
Think before reacting	Consider someone's point of view

What do you want to remember about today?

_____

_____

_____

_____

_____

_____

_____

_____

What made you smile today?

_____

_____

Draw or write about it below.

How did it make you feel?

_____

_____

Happiness

The Music in Me

Lily received a brown violin as a birthday present. She was afraid to hold the instrument. Lily was unsure if her fingers would reach the strings to play. She was uncertain if she should be happy with the birthday gift. Lily spends time talking with her family and listening to music. She is learning how to read music and play the violin.

Lily is a talented kid with a fantastic ability to play the violin. She is grateful for receiving the violin. She is learning that playing the violin is a process. Lily's self-esteem and confidence are growing each day. The violin is helping Lily to build new friendships at P.S. 411 Elementary. She is no longer afraid of meeting new people and communicating her feelings.

MY DAILY JOURNAL

Today is _____

The weather was ☀️ ⛅ 🌬️ ☁️ 🌧️ ❄️

I was feeling ☺️ 😍 😮 😎 😔 😲 😂

Circle three positive words that describe you today

Brave	Joyful	Intelligent	Super	Kind
Leader	Happy	Friendly	Honest	Courageous
Responsible	Amazing	Cheerful	Caring	Trustworthy
Considerate	Great	Smart	Strong	Awesome
Respectful	Compassionate	Helpful	Dedicated	Love

What was the best part of your day?

Draw a picture of how you feel today?

Today my biggest challenge was

_____

What was the best solution to solve my challenge?

_____

Suggestions

Talk to a friend	Exercise
Talk with an adult	Go for a walk
Write in my journal	Cool off
Take a deep breath	Listen
Think before reacting	Consider someone's point of view

What do you want to remember about today?

_____

_____

_____

_____

_____

_____

_____

_____

What is your favorite season?

_____

_____

Draw or write about it below.

How does it make you feel?

_____

_____

Do you have a stuffed animal?

_____

_____

Draw or write about it below.

How does it make you feel?

_____

_____

MY DAILY JOURNAL

Today is _____

The weather was ☀ ☁ 🌤 ⛅ 🌧 ❄

I was feeling 😊 😍 😳 😎 😔 😮 😂

Circle three positive words that describe you today

Brave	Joyful	Intelligent	Super	Kind
Leader	Happy	Friendly	Honest	Courageous
Responsible	Amazing	Cheerful	Caring	Trustworthy
Considerate	Great	Smart	Strong	Awesome
Respectful	Compassionate	Helpful	Dedicated	Love

What was the best part of your day?

Draw a picture of how you feel today?

Today my biggest challenge was

_____

What was the best solution to solve my challenge?

_____

Suggestions

Talk to a friend	Exercise
Talk with an adult	Go for a walk
Write in my journal	Cool off
Take a deep breath	Listen
Think before reacting	Consider someone's point of view

What do you want to remember about today?

_____

_____

_____

_____

_____

_____

_____

What are the names of three people to take a selfie picture with you?

_____

_____

Draw or write about it below.

How do they make you feel?

_____

_____

What are you grateful for today?

_____

_____

Draw or write about it below.

How does it make you feel?

_____

_____

MY DAILY JOURNAL

Today is _____

The weather was ☀️ ☁️ 🌬️ 🌥️ 🌧️ ❄️

I was feeling 😌 😍 😳 😎 😔 😮 😂

Circle three positive words that describe you today

Brave	Joyful	Intelligent	Super	Kind
Leader	Happy	Friendly	Honest	Courageous
Responsible	Amazing	Cheerful	Caring	Trustworthy
Considerate	Great	Smart	Strong	Awesome
Respectful	Compassionate	Helpful	Dedicated	Love

What was the best part of your day?

Draw a picture of how you feel today?

Today my biggest challenge was

_____

What was the best solution to solve my challenge?

_____

Suggestions

Talk to a friend	Exercise
Talk with an adult	Go for a walk
Write in my journal	Cool off
Take a deep breath	Listen
Think before reacting	Consider someone's point of view

What do you want to remember about today?

_____

_____

_____

_____

_____

_____

_____

_____

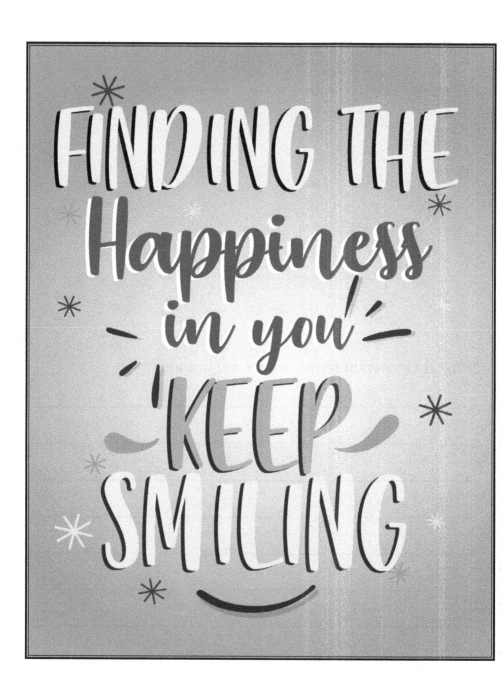

Try a Fun Activity

How Would You Plan the Happiest Saturday EVER?

Speak with your caregiver while planning this activity.

Date: _____

3 Priorities
- ☐ _____
- ☐ _____
- ☐ _____

To Do List
- ☐ _____
- ☐ _____
- ☐ _____
- ☐ _____

Exercise and Health
- ☐ Running
- ☐ Fitness
- ☐ Stretching

3 Things I am thankful for today
1. _____
2. _____
3. _____

Comments:

Plans and Schedules

6:00 AM _____
7:00 AM _____
8:00 AM _____
9:00 AM _____
10:00 AM _____
11:00 AM _____
12:00 PM _____
1:00 PM _____
2:00 PM _____
3:00 PM _____
4:00 PM _____
5:00 PM _____
6:00 PM _____
7:00 PM _____
8:00 PM _____
9:00 PM _____
10:00 PM _____

Notes:

What is your budget? _____

Who would you invite? _____

What was your biggest challenge? _____

_____

What are three ways to become a better friend?

_____

_____

Draw or write about it below.

How does it make you feel?

_____

_____

What is the name of your community library?

_____

_____

Draw or write about it below.

Do you have a library card to check out books?

_____

_____

MY DAILY JOURNAL

Today is _____

The weather was ☀️ ⛅ 🌬️ ☁️ 🌧️ ❄️

I was feeling 😌 😍 😲 😎 😔 😮 😂

Circle three positive words that describe you today

Brave	Joyful	Intelligent	Super	Kind
Leader	Happy	Friendly	Honest	Courageous
Responsible	Amazing	Cheerful	Caring	Trustworthy
Considerate	Great	Smart	Strong	Awesome
Respectful	Compassionate	Helpful	Dedicated	Love

What was the best part of your day?

Draw a picture of how you feel today?

Today my biggest challenge was

_____

What was the best solution to solve my challenge?

_____

Suggestions

Talk to a friend	Exercise
Talk with an adult	Go for a walk
Write in my journal	Cool off
Take a deep breath	Listen
Think before reacting	Consider someone's point of view

What do you want to remember about today?

_____

_____

_____

_____

_____

_____

_____

_____

What are three flavors of gum you enjoy chewing?

_____

_____

Draw or write about it below.

What is your favorite flavor?

_____

_____

Do you recycle paper at home or school?

_____

_____

Draw or write about it below.

How does it make you feel?

_____

_____

MY DAILY JOURNAL

Today is _____

The weather was ☀️ ⛅ 🌬️ ☁️ 🌧️ ❄️

I was feeling 😊 😍 😮 😎 😌 😯 😂

Circle three positive words that describe you today

Brave	Joyful	Intelligent	Super	Kind
Leader	Happy	Friendly	Honest	Courageous
Responsible	Amazing	Cheerful	Caring	Trustworthy
Considerate	Great	Smart	Strong	Awesome
Respectful	Compassionate	Helpful	Dedicated	Love

What was the best part of your day?

Draw a picture of how you feel today?

Today my biggest challenge was

_____

What was the best solution to solve my challenge?

_____

Suggestions

Talk to a friend	Exercise
Talk with an adult	Go for a walk
Write in my journal	Cool off
Take a deep breath	Listen
Think before reacting	Consider someone's point of view

What do you want to remember about today?

_____

_____

_____

_____

_____

_____

_____

What is the name of the coolest kid at school?

_____

_____

Draw or write about it below.

How do they make you feel?

_____

_____

What is the name of your pet?

_____

_____

Draw or write about it below.

How often do you spend time with your pet at home?

_____

_____

What are your superpowers?

_____

_____

Draw or write about it below.

How do they make you feel?

_____

_____

MY DAILY JOURNAL

Today is _____

The weather was ☀️ ☁️ 🌬️ ⛅ 🌧️ ❄️

I was feeling 😌 😍 😳 😎 😔 😮 😂

Circle three positive words that describe you today

Brave	Joyful	Intelligent	Super	Kind
Leader	Happy	Friendly	Honest	Courageous
Responsible	Amazing	Cheerful	Caring	Trustworthy
Considerate	Great	Smart	Strong	Awesome
Respectful	Compassionate	Helpful	Dedicated	Love

What was the best part of your day?

Draw a picture of how you feel today?

Today my biggest challenge was

_____

What was the best solution to solve my challenge?

_____

Suggestions

Talk to a friend	Exercise
Talk with an adult	Go for a walk
Write in my journal	Cool off
Take a deep breath	Listen
Think before reacting	Consider someone's point of view

What do you want to remember about today?

_____

_____

_____

_____

_____

_____

_____

_____

What is the funniest joke you shared with family or friends?

_____

_____

Draw or write about it below.

Why was the joke funny?

_____

_____

HAPPINESS
IS
HOMEMADE

FOLLOW YOUR DREAMS

Try a
Fun Activity
Cursive Writing

Use the alphabets below and trace the letters.

Aa Bb Cc Dd Ee

Ff Gg Hh Ii Jj Kk

Ll Mm Nn Oo Pp

Qq Rr Ss Tt Uu

Vv Ww Xx Yy Zz

Now it's your turn to practice writing in cursive.

Word	Cursive
between	
brave	
through	
change	
would	
people	

Let's help the Bayside Bunch practice
writing their names in cursive.

Print Name	Cursive Name
Selwyn	
Grace	
QB	
Chico	
Lily	

Let's try writing your name, and the name(s)
of your brother, sister, pet, and best friend in cursive.

Print Name	Practice Cursive

Let's write some of your favorite things in cursive!

Print Word	Cursive Word

DON'T MISS A SINGLE ADVENTURE WITH

The Bayside Bunch

PLEASE DON'T FORGET TO LEAVE REVIEWS

Now available at thebaysidebunch.com

DON'T MISS A SINGLE ADVENTURE WITH

The Bayside Bunch

PLEASE DON'T FORGET TO LEAVE REVIEWS

Now available at thebaysidebunch.com

About the Author

Dr. Unseld Robinson is an urban educator and author of the *Bayside Bunch Diverse Children's Book Series*. He focuses on kindness and diversity in each children's book. For the past 20 years, Dr. Robinson has been helping children celebrate diversity and making positive connections with peers of different ethnicities. He believes leveraging student strengths and seeing themselves in the story as main characters is important. Children will be comfortable engaging with the text, having responses, strengthening their voices, and building confidence. *The Bayside Bunch Series* uses relatable characters that children know and a school environment that they will recognize immediately.

Learn more about Dr. Robinson and *The Bayside Bunch* series at thebaysidebunch.com, Instagram, and on Facebook.

La Sirena™
BOOKS

thebaysidebunch.com

Instagram:
@ lasirenabooks

Find us on Facebook
@ lasirenabooks01